Grade 6

The Syllabus of [illegible] details of requirements, es[illegible] aural tests and sight-reading. Attention should be paid to the Special Notices on the front inside cover, where warning is given of changes.

The syllabus is obtainable from music dealers or from The Associated Board of the Royal Schools of Music, 14 Bedford Square, London WC1B 3JG (please send a stamped addressed C5 envelope).

In overseas centres, information may be obtained from the Local Representative or Resident Secretary.

Requirements

SCALES AND ARPEGGIOS (from memory)

Scales

(i) in similar motion, hands together one octave apart, and each hand separately, legato, in *all* keys, major and minor (melodic *and* harmonic) (four octaves)
(ii) each hand separately, staccato, in the keys specified in one of the following groups chosen by the candidate (four octaves):
Group 1: C, A, F♯, E♭ majors
Group 2: G, E, B♭, D♭ majors
(iii) in contrary motion, both hands beginning and ending on the key-note (unison), legato, in the major and harmonic minor keys of the group chosen for (ii) (two octaves)
(iv) in thirds, each hand separately (fingered 2 & 4), staccato, in the key of C major (two octaves)

Chromatic Scales

(i) in similar motion, hands together one octave apart, and each hand separately, legato, beginning on any note named by the examiner (four octaves)
(ii) in contrary motion, legato, both hands beginning and ending on C (L.H.) and E (R.H.), a third apart (two octaves)

Arpeggios

in similar motion, hands together one octave apart, and each hand separately, legato:
(i) the major and minor common chords of *all* keys, in root position only (four octaves)
(ii) diminished seventh chords beginning on B, C♯, D♯ and E (three octaves)

PLAYING AT SIGHT (see current syllabus)

AURAL TESTS (see current syllabus)

THREE PIECES

Candidates should choose one piece from Group A, one piece from Group B, and the third piece *either* from Group C *or* from the further alternatives listed below:

Mendelssohn Lied ohne Worte, Op. 19 No. 4
H. Hofmann Zur Laute (To the Lute), Op. 37 No. 1
These are included in A Romantic Sketchbook for Piano, Book IV, *published by the Associated Board*

Editor for the Associated Board: **Richard Jones**

Music origination by Barnes Music Engraving Ltd.
Printed in Great Britain by Headley Brothers Ltd, The Invicta Press, Ashford, Kent and London.

Where appropriate, pieces have been checked with original source material and edited as necessary for instructional purposes. Fingering, phrasing, pedalling, metronome marks and the editorial realization of ornaments (where given) are for guidance but are not comprehensive or obligatory.

A:1

L'Atalante

F. COUPERIN

Source: *Second livre de pièces de clavecin* (Paris, 1717).
Wilfrid Mellers says of this piece: 'Presumably the fleet Atlanta of classical antiquity is depicted, though a reference to some Atlanta-like contemporary may also be implicit'. Music from the French Baroque is distinguished by its ornate style and ornamentation. All ornaments in this edition are original; however, for the purposes of the examination those in round brackets may be omitted without penalty. In the left hand of bars 22–6 and 42–50 and the right hand of bars 30–1, the fingering is Couperin's (from his treatise *L'Art de toucher le clavecin*). This indicates the kind of articulation he requires, e.g. slurred pairs in the second half of bars 30 and 31, whole-bar groups in the left hand of bars 42 ff. Bracketed modern alternatives are given in bars 22–6. Unslurred quavers should be mostly detached. Dynamics are left to the player's discretion.

Fin

A:2

Sonata in F

Kp. 378

D. SCARLATTI

Source: Parma MSS, Vol. X, No. 21.
The clearly sectional structure invites overall dynamic contrasts: perhaps ***f*** for the major-key opening theme, ***p*** for the tonic-minor secondary theme (bar 20) and a return to ***f*** for the major-key coda (bar 43). A similar scheme might be adopted in the second half of the piece. Some variation within each section would be effective, for example ***mf*** in bar 9, ***f*** in bar 13, ***mp*** in bar 15 and a *crescendo* in bar 17 to ***f*** in bar 19.

123
1
52
1 3
4
32
5
3
57

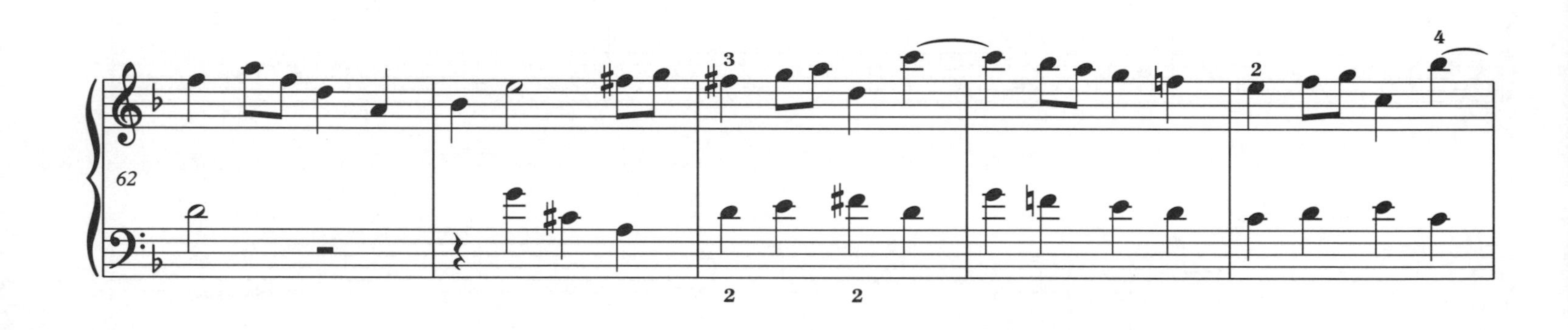
3
4
2
62
2 2

3
3
2 4
1 4
67
2 1
1

5
71

76
81
85
90
94

[Allegro moderato]

First movement from Sonata in D, Hob. XVI/4

Edited by
Howard Ferguson

HAYDN

Source: *Divertimento in D dur per il Clavi-Cembalo*, Vienna, Gesellschaft der Musikfreunde, MS VII 15676.
This is an early harpsichord sonata, written some time around 1766 when Haydn was appointed Capellmeister to Prince Esterházy. Dynamics are editorial suggestions only.

Reprinted from Haydn, *Selected Keyboard Sonatas*, Book I, edited by Howard Ferguson (Associated Board)

tr
tr
tr
cresc.

cresc.
cresc.

44
fp
cresc.
47
f
p
50
cresc.
f
p
53
f
tr
p
55
f
tr

B:2

Rondo

Third movement from Sonatina in G, Op. 88 No. 2

Edited by
Lionel Salter

KUHLAU

Source: *4 sonatines*, Op. 88 (Copenhagen, 1827).
Kuhlau, a contemporary of Beethoven, moved in 1810 from his native Germany to Denmark, where he became a celebrated pianist and composer.

Reprinted from Kuhlau, *Four Sonatinas*, Op. 88, edited by Lionel Salter (Associated Board)

26
32
f
38
p
45
51
cresc.
f
p

sf
dolce
sf
p

mf
f

Dance

No. 2 from *Three Dances*

JURRIAAN ANDRIESSEN

29
34
molto dim. e molto rit.
39
a tempo
espr.
44
simile
49
poco rit.
CODA
molto rit.
ppp

C:2

Prelude in A flat

Op. 34 No. 17

SHOSTAKOVICH

a tempo
accelerando
rit.
dim.
mf
dim.
a tempo largo
cresc.
rit.
dim.
p
pp